Boc

IN RECITAL
Throughout the Year™
(with Performance Strategies)

Volume One

ABOUT THE SERIES • A NOTE TO THE TEACHER

In Recital — Throughout the Year™ is a series that focuses on fabulous repertoire, intended to motivate your students. We know that to motivate, the teacher must challenge the student with attainable goals. This series makes that possible. The fine composers and arrangers of this series have created musically engaging pieces, which have been carefully leveled and address the technical strengths and weaknesses of students. The wide range of styles in each book of the series complements other FJH publications and will help you to plan students' recital repertoire for the entire year. You will find original solos and duets that focus on different musical and technical issues, giving you the selection needed to accommodate your students' needs. There are arrangements of famous classical themes, as well as repertoire written for Halloween, Christmas, and Fourth of July recitals. In this way, your student will have recital pieces throughout the entire year! Additionally, the series provides a progressive discussion on the art of performance. The earlier levels offer tips on recital preparation, while the later levels address more advanced technical and psychological issues that help to realize successful performances.

 Use the enclosed CD as a teaching and motivational tool. Have your students listen to the recording and discuss interpretation with you!

THE
F·J·H
MUSIC
COMPANY
INC.

Production: Frank and Gail Hackinson
Production Coordinators: Philip Groeber and Isabel Otero Bowen
Cover: Terpstra Design, San Francisco
Cover Piano Illustration: Keith Criss
Text Design and Layout: Maritza Cosano Gomez
Engraving: Kevin Olson and Tempo Music Press, Inc.
Printer: Tempo Music Press, Inc.

ISBN 1-56939-438-5

Copyright © 2004 The FJH Music Company Inc.
2525 Davie Road, Suite 360, Fort Lauderdale, Florida 33317-7424
International Copyright Secured. All Rights Reserved. Printed in U.S.A.
WARNING! The music, text, design, and graphics in this publication
are protected by copyright law. Any duplication is an infringement of
U.S. copyright law.

9 RECITAL PREPARATION TIPS • FOR THE TEACHER

1. Consider a tiered approach to developing comfort in performance. Make "mini" performances a regular occurrence, probably without even calling them performances. Have a student play for the student who follows his/her lesson. It doesn't matter if their leveling is different; the older students are naturally nice to the young and the young provide a non-threatening audience for the older. Have students play mini concerts at home. Younger students may enjoy concerts for their favorite stuffed animals each day after practice. Advise older students to practice performing by recording themselves. Of course, you will tailor these suggestions according to each student's personality. Just remember, *no venue is too small and frequency is the key*. Suggestions for mini-performances and performance strategies are also addressed in "A Note to Students" on pages 16 and 17, and "Steps for a Winning Performance" on page 28.

   Once students are comfortable with these "mini" performances, teachers must create opportunities for students to play in public, so that they will get used to the idea of getting up on stage and playing for others. Studio group lessons or performance classes are perfect for trial performances, then take it to the next step and invite family or friends to a performance class.

   Try these different performance venues and you will be pleased with the results. The "tiered" approach helps performance to become a natural part of piano study.

2. Make sure that your students have the opportunity to perform pieces well within their technical range. These performances will help build student confidence and will make a huge difference when they are playing more challenging repertoire.

3. Have students practice concentrating on the tempo, mood, and dynamics of the piece before beginning to play.

4. Coach students on how to walk purposefully *to* the piano, adjust the bench, and check their position relative to the piano. Have them practice this a lot in the lesson and at home. Familiarity with the process really helps.

5. Talk to your students about how to finish the piece. Coach them to stay with the music until the piece is over. Discuss how they will move at the end of the piece: i.e., quickly moving the hands away from the keyboard, or slowly lifting the hands with the lifting of the pedal, depending on the repertoire.

6. Coach students how to bow and walk purposefully *away* from the piano. Again, practice this together often so that it feels natural to them.

7. Remind students to keep the recital in perspective. The recital piece should be one of several the student is working on, so that they understand that there is "life after the recital."

8. If possible, have a practice session in the performance location. Encourage your students to focus on what they can control and remind them that although a piano may feel differently, their technique will not "go away."

9. Have your students listen to the companion CD. Not only does this give them ideas on how to interpret the pieces, it builds an intuitive knowledge of how the pieces sound, which helps increase confidence and comfort.

The goal is to instill in our students the excitement of playing for others and to demystify the process. There is nothing quite like communicating a piece of music to an audience and then enjoying their positive reaction to it. With our help, our students can perform up to their potential in public and enjoy this exciting and rewarding experience.

ORGANIZATION OF THE SERIES
IN RECITAL • THROUGHOUT THE YEAR™

*I*n Recital — *Throughout the Year*™ is carefully leveled into the following categories: Early Elementary, Elementary, Late Elementary, Early Intermediate, Intermediate, and Late Intermediate. Each of the works has been selected for its artistic as well as its pedagogical merit.

Book Three — Late Elementary, reinforces the following concepts:

- Eighth notes are added to the basic notes students played in books 1 and 2. The dotted quarter note is introduced in the last piece of the book.

- Students play different articulations such as *legato* and *staccato* at the same time.

- Students play pieces in a variety of different moods, tempos, and forms.

- Students play blocked and broken major, minor, and diminished chords.

- Pieces reinforce five-finger scales, as well as scale patterns that extend from the usual five-finger patterns (with finger crossings).

- Blocked intervals up to a sixth, double thirds, and hand-over-hand arpeggios are played.

- Students continue to experience movement up and down the keyboard. The use of the pedal is continued and expanded to create a big sound as well as to play artistically.

- Pieces continue to reinforce basic musical terminology and symbols such as *crescendo, decrescendo, ritardando, fermata, mezzo forte, mezzo piano, forte, piano, fortissimo, pianissimo,* and *D.C. al fine.*

- Keys of C major, G major, F major, D major, A minor, and D minor.

Most of the pieces in Book Three are solos. *Song of the Sahara* was composed as an equal part duet. Some of the solos have optional teacher accompaniments to enhance the overall sound of the piece.

TABLE OF CONTENTS

Autumn Colors

Judith R. Strickland

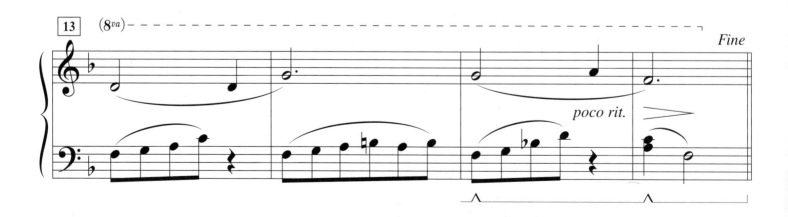

Copyright © 2004 The FJH Music Company Inc.
2525 Davie Road, Suite 360, Fort Lauderdale, Florida 33317-7424
FF1461   International Copyright Secured.   Made in U.S.A.   All Rights Reserved.

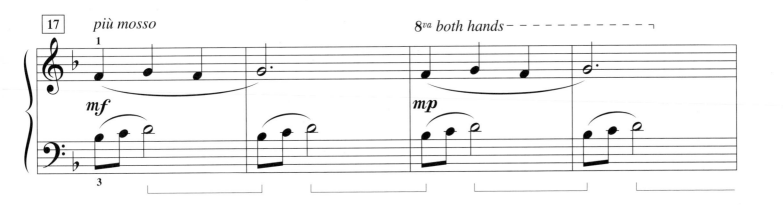

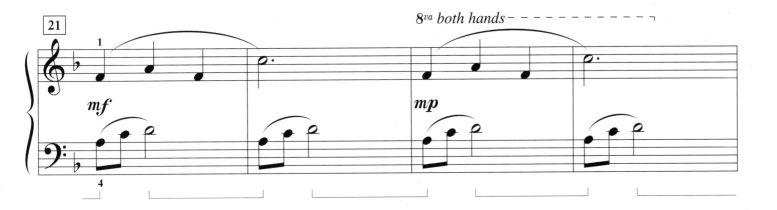

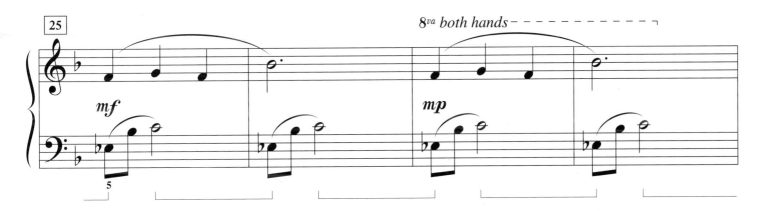

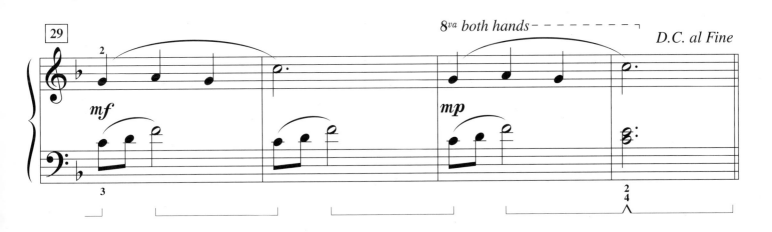

RAINDROPS ON MY ROOF

Kevin Olson

In two; quickly and evenly (♩ = 120 or faster)

Copyright © 2004 The FJH Music Company Inc.
2525 Davie Road, Suite 360, Fort Lauderdale, Florida 33317-7424
International Copyright Secured.   Made in U.S.A.   All Rights Reserved.

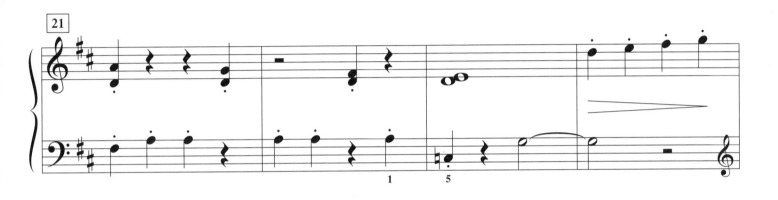

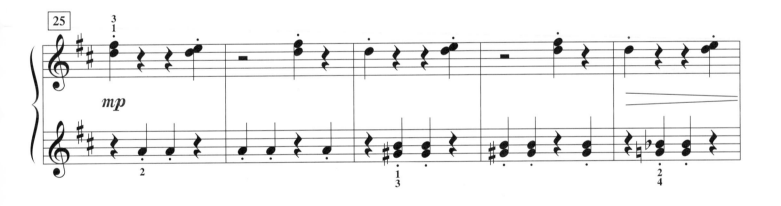

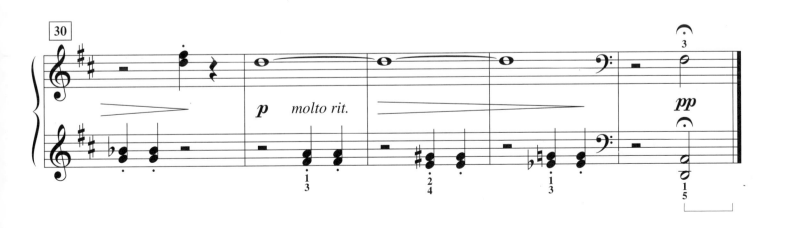

Song of the Sahara
Secondo

Kevin Olson

Mysteriously (♩ = 120-132)

Play both hands one octave lower throughout

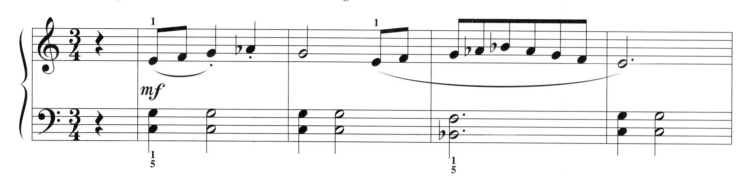

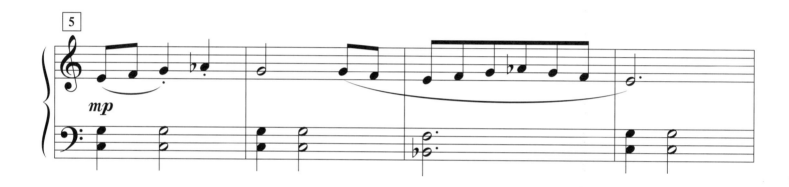

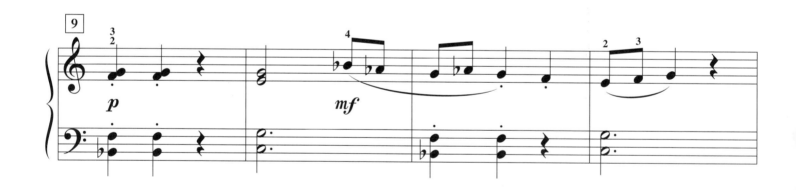

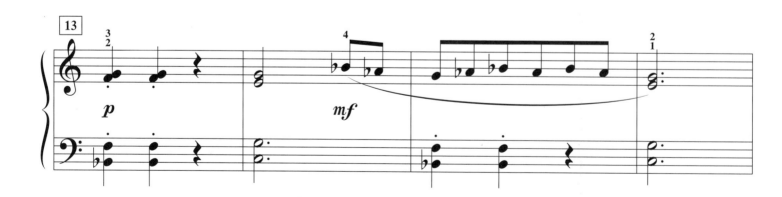

Copyright © 2004 The FJH Music Company Inc.
2525 Davie Road, Suite 360, Fort Lauderdale, Florida 33317-7424
International Copyright Secured.   Made in U.S.A.   All Rights Reserved.

Song of the Sahara
Primo

Kevin Olson

Mysteriously (♩ = 120-132)

Play both hands one octave higher throughout

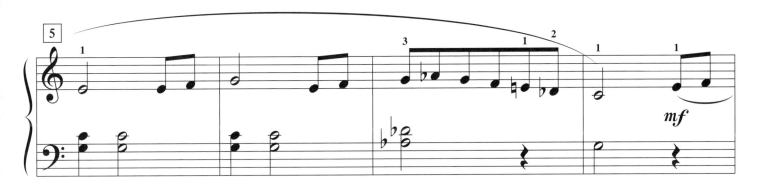

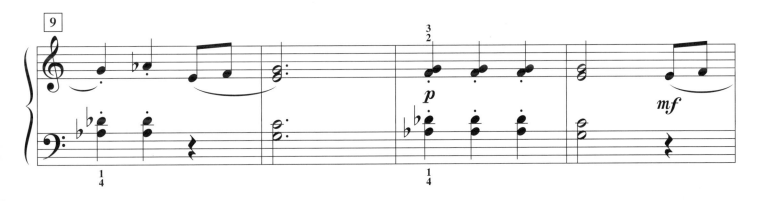

Copyright © 2004 The FJH Music Company Inc.
2525 Davie Road, Suite 360, Fort Lauderdale, Florida 33317-7424
International Copyright Secured.   Made in U.S.A.   All Rights Reserved.   FF1461

Secondo

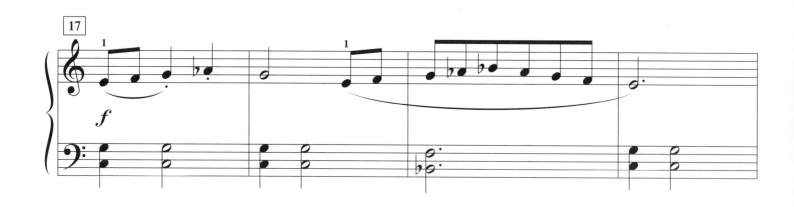

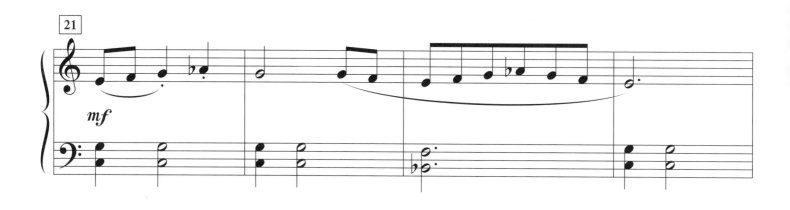

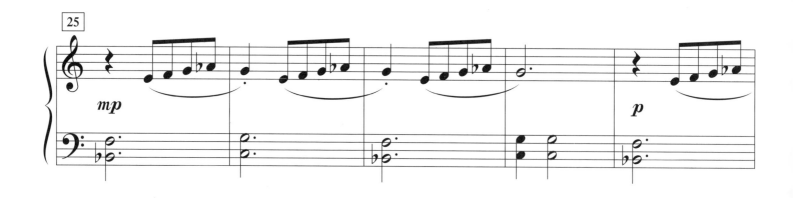

Primo

O MIO BABBINO CARO

O my dear father
from the opera, *Gianni Schicchi*

Giacomo Puccini
arr. Edwin McLean

Andantino; cantabile (♩ = 120-132)

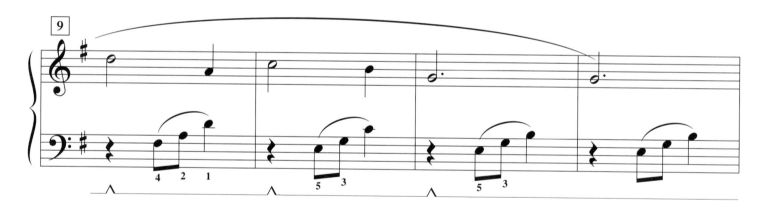

This arrangement © 2004 Frank J. Hackinson Publishing Co.
2525 Davie Road, Suite 360, Fort Lauderdale, Florida 33317-7424
International Copyright Secured.   Made in U.S.A.   All Rights Reserved.

A NOTE TO STUDENTS

Welcome to the wonderful world of performing. Performing in public is a special skill that can be learned, just like learning how to swim! It might seem a bit scary at first, but once you learn this skill, performing can be a whole lot of fun!

Here are two keys to successful and enjoyable performances:
- Prepare well before hand
- Practice performing in front of others

Preparation:

Here is a list of things to do to make sure you know your piece extremely well: (Place a check in the box each day you complete the task and start four weeks before the recital.)

4 weeks	3 weeks	2 weeks	1 week

Can you play the entire piece, hands alone, *from memory?* (Listening to each individual part helps you to be completely aware of what each hand is playing.)

Can you sing or hum the melody away from the piano?

Can you start your piece at four *different* places in the music? (You and your teacher can mark with a star ☆ four good starting places).

Can you play the piece from beginning to end at "half tempo"? ("Half tempo" means to play it with all of the correct rhythms, notes, and dynamics, but at half of the speed you would play it when performing it.)

After playing the piece, ask yourself: Did it sound like the title suggests? Did I bring the piece to life?

Listen to the recording of your recital piece for ideas on how to play it. You can mark directly in your score what you hear.

Starting four weeks before your actual performance, practice these strategies every day. It might be difficult to do all of these at first, but the more you practice, the easier they will become. Remember, if you prepare well, the performance day will be easy and fun!

> You can use these two pages as a practice guide for every recital piece you play in this book!

Two weeks before your recital, try these two performance tips:

1. Every *other* day, play your piece through three times in a row, without stopping. Pretend you are playing in the recital. If you make a little mistake, just keep going. This practice strategy helps you to learn how you will feel when you are performing your piece(s) in a recital, in front of an audience.

2 weeks... 2 tips...

- *play your piece through three times in a row...*

    pretend you are playing in the recital...

- *play in front of an audience...*

    if you make a little mistake, just keep going...

Then, *after* the three performances, think about the following questions and answer them below:

Did I play my pieces steadily, making sure that they were rhythmically accurate? (Could I easily hear every single note in the pieces? Was everything clear?) If not, what could I have done better?

_____

Did I play my pieces beautifully, with a good sound at every moment? If not, what could I have done better?

_____

Did I play the *forte* sections really *forte* and the *piano* sections really *piano*?

_____

Was I nervous? Excited? Happy with what I could play?

_____

(Your teacher will give you some great input on this question and your answer!)

2. Make arrangements to play in front of an audience. (Your teacher will help you with this!) Part of the fun of learning how to play the piano is to share the music with others!

Write below the places where you performed your piece(s). After the place, describe the audience's reaction to your playing (they clapped, they smiled, etc.)

_____

_____

_____

To learn the **Steps for a Winning Performance,** turn to page 28.

Theme from Symphony No. 40

Wolfgang A. Mozart
arr. Timothy Brown

Moderato (♩ = 144-152)

Teacher Accompaniment: (*Student plays one octave higher*)

To Coda ⊕

This arrangement © 2004 The FJH Music Company Inc.
2525 Davie Road, Suite 360, Fort Lauderdale, Florida 33317-7424
International Copyright Secured.   Made in U.S.A.   All Rights Reserved.

FF1461

ALLEGRETTO

from Symphony No. 7,
second movement

Ludwig van Beethoven
arr. Timothy Brown

Theme

Slowly; with feeling ($\quarternote$ = 60)

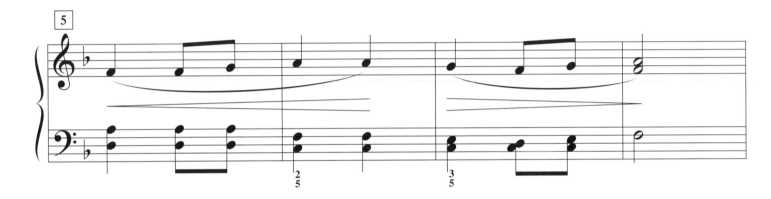

Var. 1

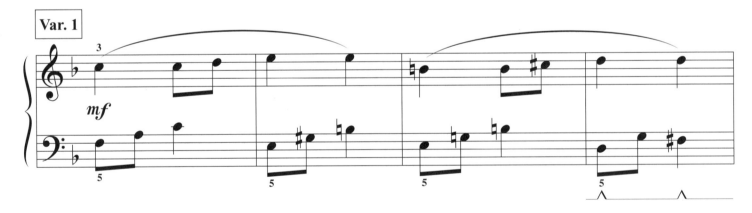

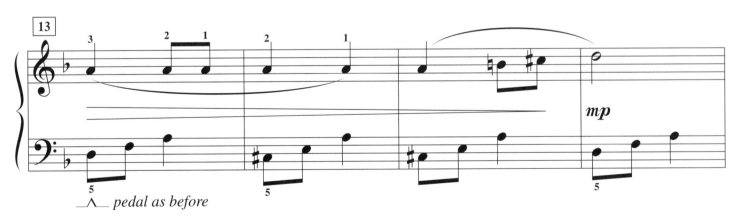

This arrangement © 2004 The FJH Music Company Inc.
2525 Davie Road, Suite 360, Fort Lauderdale, Florida 33317-7424
International Copyright Secured.   Made in U.S.A.   All Rights Reserved.

FF1461

Skeleton Stomp

Melody Bober

Copyright © 2004 The FJH Music Company Inc.
2525 Davie Road, Suite 360, Fort Lauderdale, Florida 33317-7424
International Copyright Secured.   Made in U.S.A.   All Rights Reserved.

JOSEPH, DEAREST JOSEPH MINE

Traditional German Carol
arr. Elizabeth W. Greenleaf

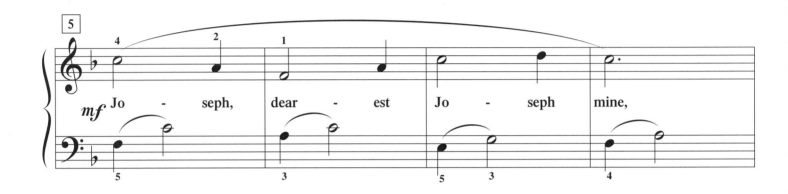

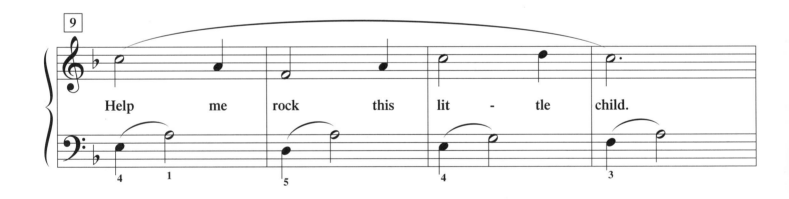

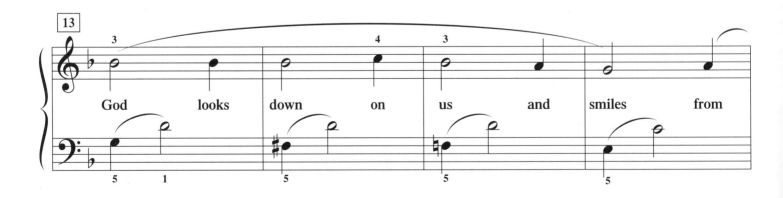

This arrangement © 2004 The FJH Music Company Inc.
2525 Davie Road, Suite 360, Fort Lauderdale, Florida 33317-7424
International Copyright Secured.   Made in U.S.A.   All Rights Reserved.

heav'n   a - bove,   so   sings   the

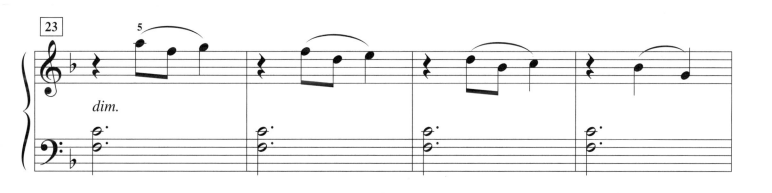

bless - ed   Ma - ry.

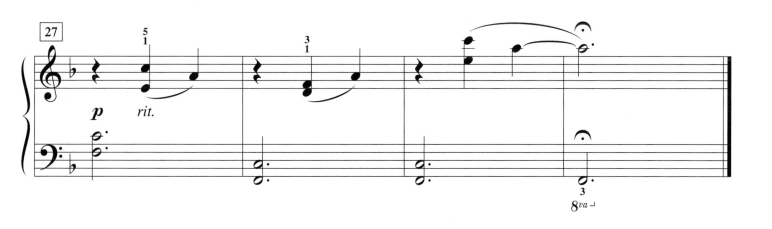

dim.

p   *rit.*

My Country, 'Tis of Thee

Words: Samuel F. Smith
Music: Thesaurus Musicus
arr. Edwin McLean

Moderately; solemnly

This arrangement © 2004 Frank J. Hackinson Publishing Co.
2525 Davie Road, Suite 360, Fort Lauderdale, Florida 33317-7424
International Copyright Secured.   Made in U.S.A.   All Rights Reserved.

My country, 'tis of thee,
Sweet land of liberty,
Of thee I sing:
Land where my fathers died,
Land of the Pilgrims' pride,
From ev'ry mountain side
Let freedom ring!

STEPS FOR A WINNING PERFORMANCE

Practice:

1. Walking to the piano with confidence and with purpose.

2. Standing in front of the piano bench, nodding your head, and smiling at the audience.

3. Sitting at the bench and making sure you are seated at the proper height as well as distance from the keyboard.

4. Thinking about the speed, mood, and dynamics of the piece; and breathing before you begin.

5. Taking your time before you begin. This adds drama and excitement to your performance, and helps you to completely focus.

6. Staying with the music while you play! This means that you think about the notes, dynamics, and phrasing as you play, you feel the emotion of the music, and listen to yourself every single moment.

7. Listening to yourself produce a beautiful sound at all times!

8. Placing your hands in your lap after you finish playing. Remember to bow. It is a way to say "Thank you" to your audience for listening.

ABOUT THE COMPOSERS/ARRANGERS

Melody Bober

Piano instructor, music teacher, composer, clinician—Melody Bober has been active in music education for over 25 years. As a composer, her goal is to create exciting and challenging pieces that are strong teaching tools to promote a lifelong love, understanding, and appreciation for music. Pedagogy, ear training, and musical expression are fundamentals of Melody's teaching, as well as fostering composition skills in her students.

Melody graduated with highest honors from the University of Illinois with a degree in music education, and later received a master's degree in piano performance. She maintains a large private studio, performs in numerous regional events, and conducts workshops across the country. She and her husband Jeff reside in Minnesota.

Timothy Brown

Composition has always been a natural form of self-expression for Timothy Brown. His Montessori-influenced philosophy has greatly helped define his approach as a teacher and composer of educational music. His composition originates from a love of improvisation at the piano and his personal goal of writing music that will help release the student's imagination.

Mr. Brown holds two degrees in piano performance, including a master's degree from the University of North Texas. His many honors include a "Commissioned for Clavier" magazine article, and first prize award in the Fifth Aliénor International Harpsichord Competition for his solo composition *Suite Española*. As a clinician, Mr. Brown has presented numerous clinics and most recently represented FJH Music with his presentation at the 2000 World Piano Pedagogy Conference. Currently living in Dallas, Mr. Brown teaches piano and composition at the Harry Stone Montessori Magnet School. He frequently serves as an adjudicator for piano and composition contests, and performs with his wife as duo-pianists.

Elizabeth W. Greenleaf

Elizabeth W. Greenleaf received a Piano Teaching Certificate and a Bachelor of Music degree in composition from Florida State University, and a Master of Music degree in piano performance from Louisiana State University.

Elizabeth has been active as a composer, performer, and teacher for over twenty-five years. She has performed many recitals, both as an accompanist for instrumentalists and singers, and as a chamber music player. Her students have ranged from preschoolers to senior citizens, and she has taught at all levels from beginning to advanced. Recently retired from teaching, Elizabeth enjoys composing to meet the needs of students. Her music has received high praise from top teachers throughout the country.

Edwin McLean

Edwin McLean is a freelance composer living in Chapel Hill, North Carolina. He is a graduate of the Yale School of Music, where he studied with Krzysztof Penderecki and Jacob Druckman. He also holds a master's degree in music theory and a bachelor's degree in piano performance from the University of Colorado.

The recipient of several grants and awards: The MacDowell Colony, the John Work Award, the Woods Chandler Prize (Yale), Meet the Composer, Florida Arts Council, and others, he has also won the Aliénor Composition Competition for his work Sonata for Harpsichord, published by The FJH Music Company and recorded by Elaine Funaro (Into the Millennium, Gasparo GSCD-331).

Since 1979, Edwin McLean has arranged the music of some of today's best known recording artists. Currently, he is senior editor as well as MIDI orchestrator for FJH Music.

Kevin Olson

Kevin Olson is an active pianist, composer, and faculty member at Elmhurst College near Chicago, Illinois, where he teaches classical and jazz piano, music theory, and electronic music. He holds a Doctor of Education degree from National-Louis University, and bachelor's and master's degrees in music composition and theory from Brigham Young University. Before teaching at Elmhurst College, he held a visiting professor position at Humboldt State University in California. A native of Utah, Kevin began composing at the age of five. When he was twelve, his composition *An American Trainride* received the Overall First Prize at the 1983 National PTA Convention in Albuquerque, New Mexico. Since then, he has been a composer-in-residence at the National Conference on Piano Pedagogy and has written music for the American Piano Quartet, Chicago a cappella, the Rich Matteson Jazz Festival, among others. Kevin maintains a large piano studio, teaching students of a variety of ages and abilities. Many of the needs of his own piano students have inspired his nearly forty books and solos published by The FJH Music Company Inc., which he joined as a writer in 1994.

Judith R. Strickland

Judith R. Strickland received a bachelor's degree in music from Mary Baldwin College in Staunton, Virginia, and a master's degree in sacred music from Union Theological Seminary in New York. In addition to actively teaching both piano and organ, Judith also serves as accompanist for the Community Chorus and Piedmont Choral Society, as well as for numerous instrumental and vocal soloists.